Jolly Phonics
Handwriting Book 6
y x ch sh th
in print letters

Guidelines

Good pencil control and correct formation enable students to achieve neat, fluent and, eventually, joined handwriting.

Handwriting practice works best when the students are sitting at their table or desk. This provides a firm flat surface to write on and encourages correct posture.

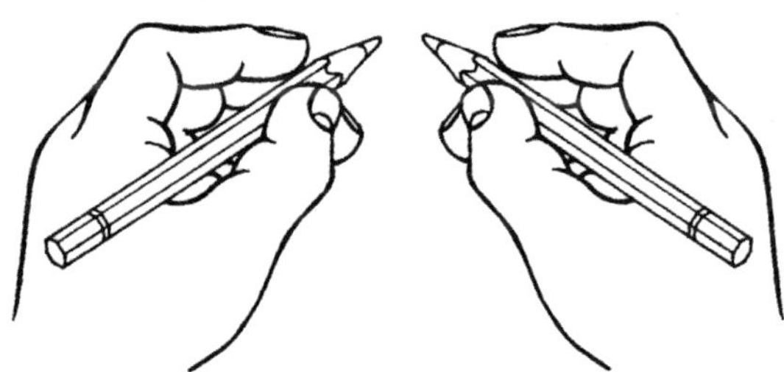

A good pencil hold from the very beginning is extremely important for developing neat, fluent handwriting. The tripod pencil grip is recommended.

Hold the pencil between the thumb and index finger, and support it on the middle finger. As the pencil is moved, the knuckles on the thumb and index finger look like a frog's legs.

Coloring is also a good way to develop fine motor skills. Encourage the students to color carefully, to keep within the lines, and to choose appropriate colors.

Spot the frog

Encourage the children to look out for the frog throughout these books, to remind them to practice their "froggy-leg" grip.

Write your name on the cake and draw candles on top to show how old you are.

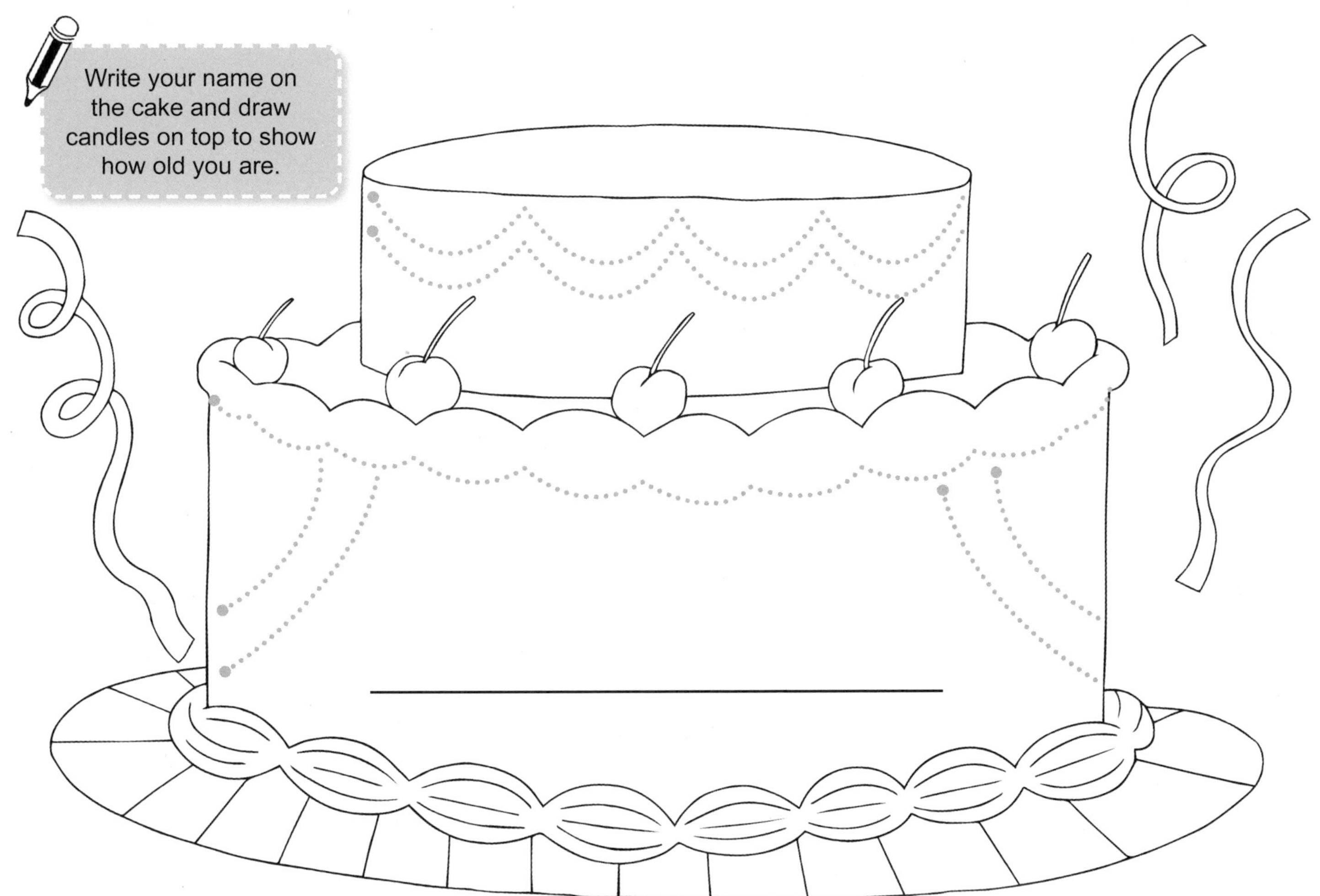

Trace the patterns and try to think of other words with these sounds in.

z z

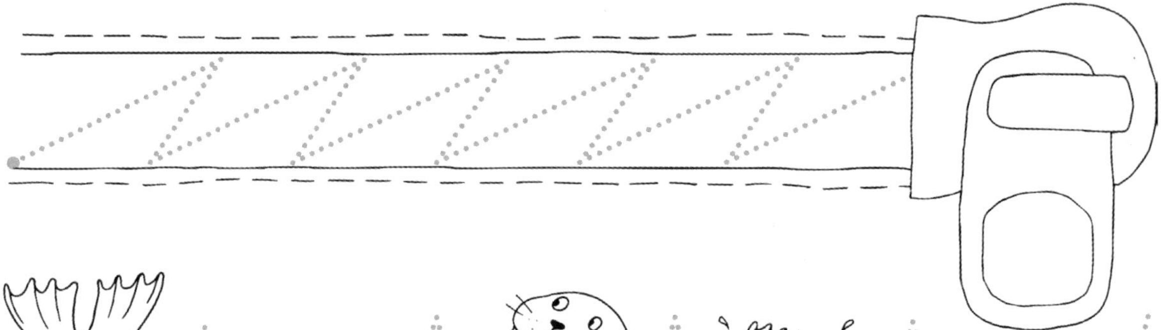

w

ng

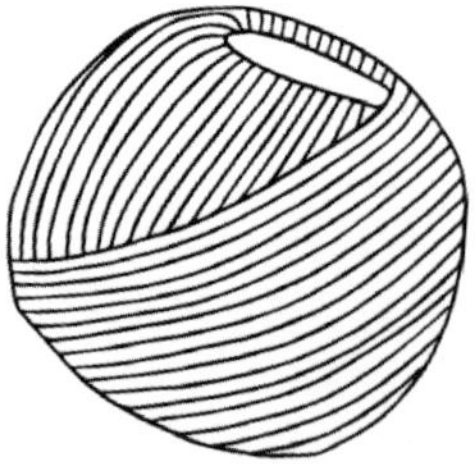

y y y y

Trace the strings of the yo-yos.

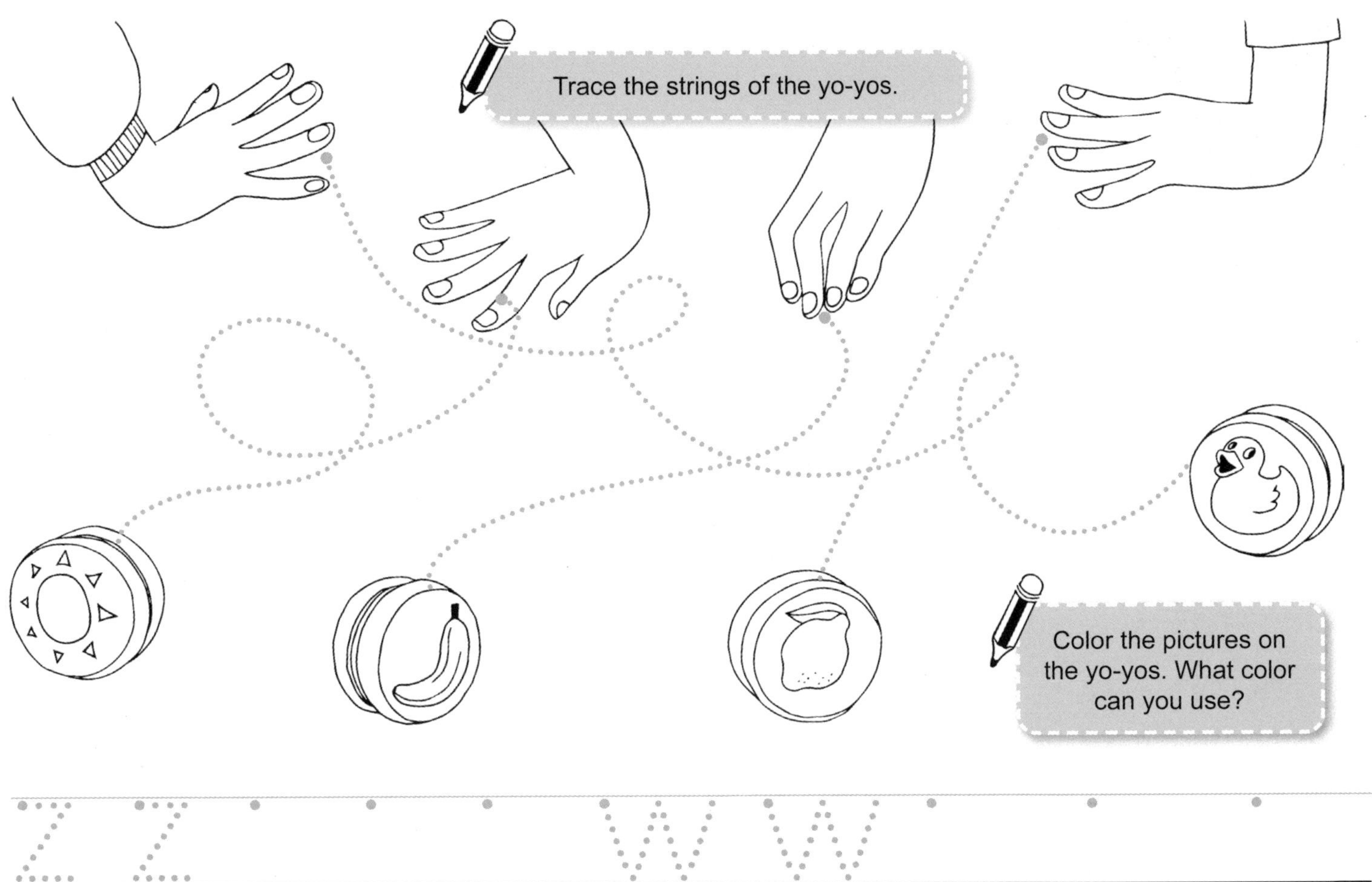

Color the pictures on the yo-yos. What color can you use?

Z Z W W

X

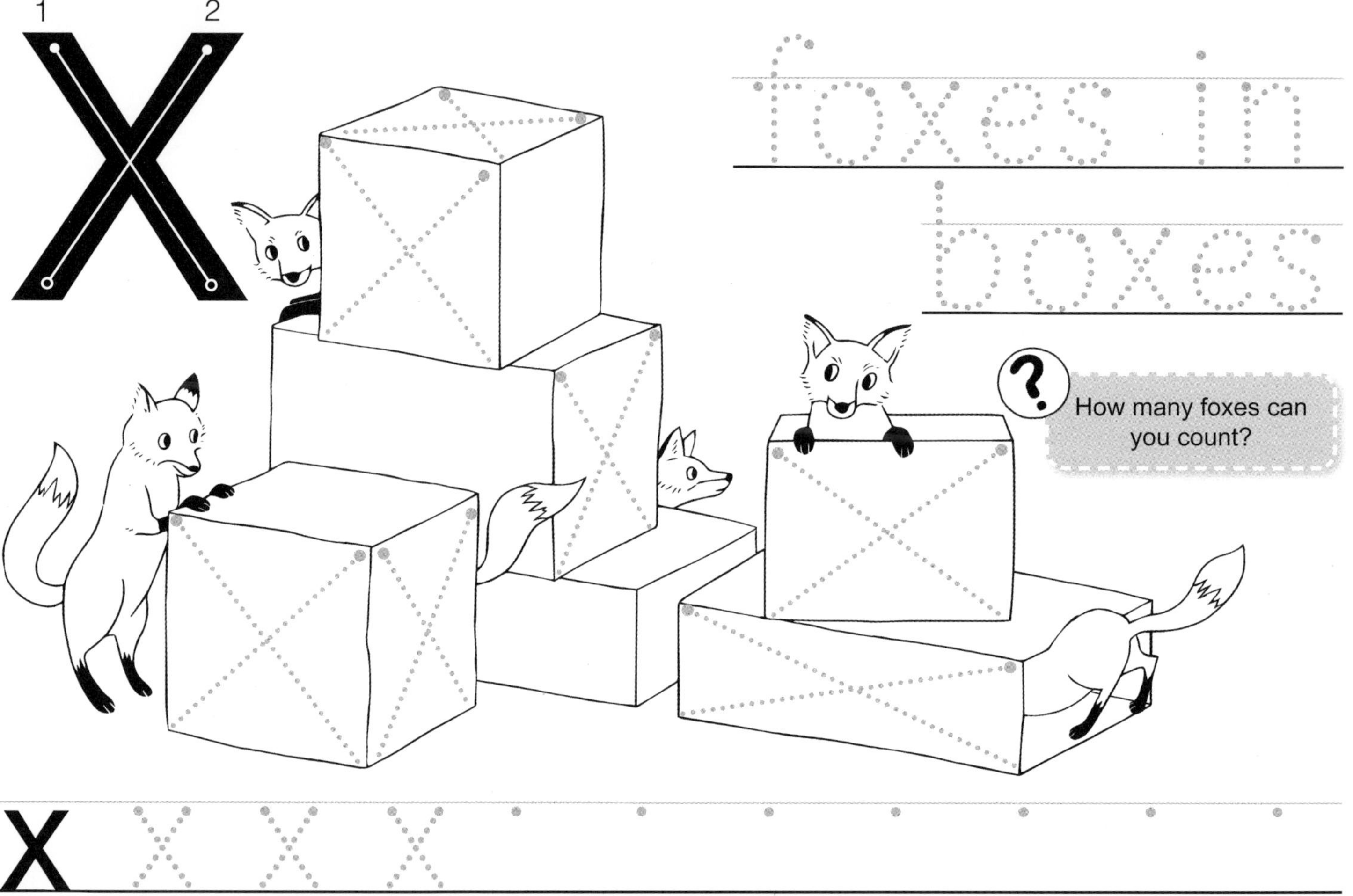

X x x x

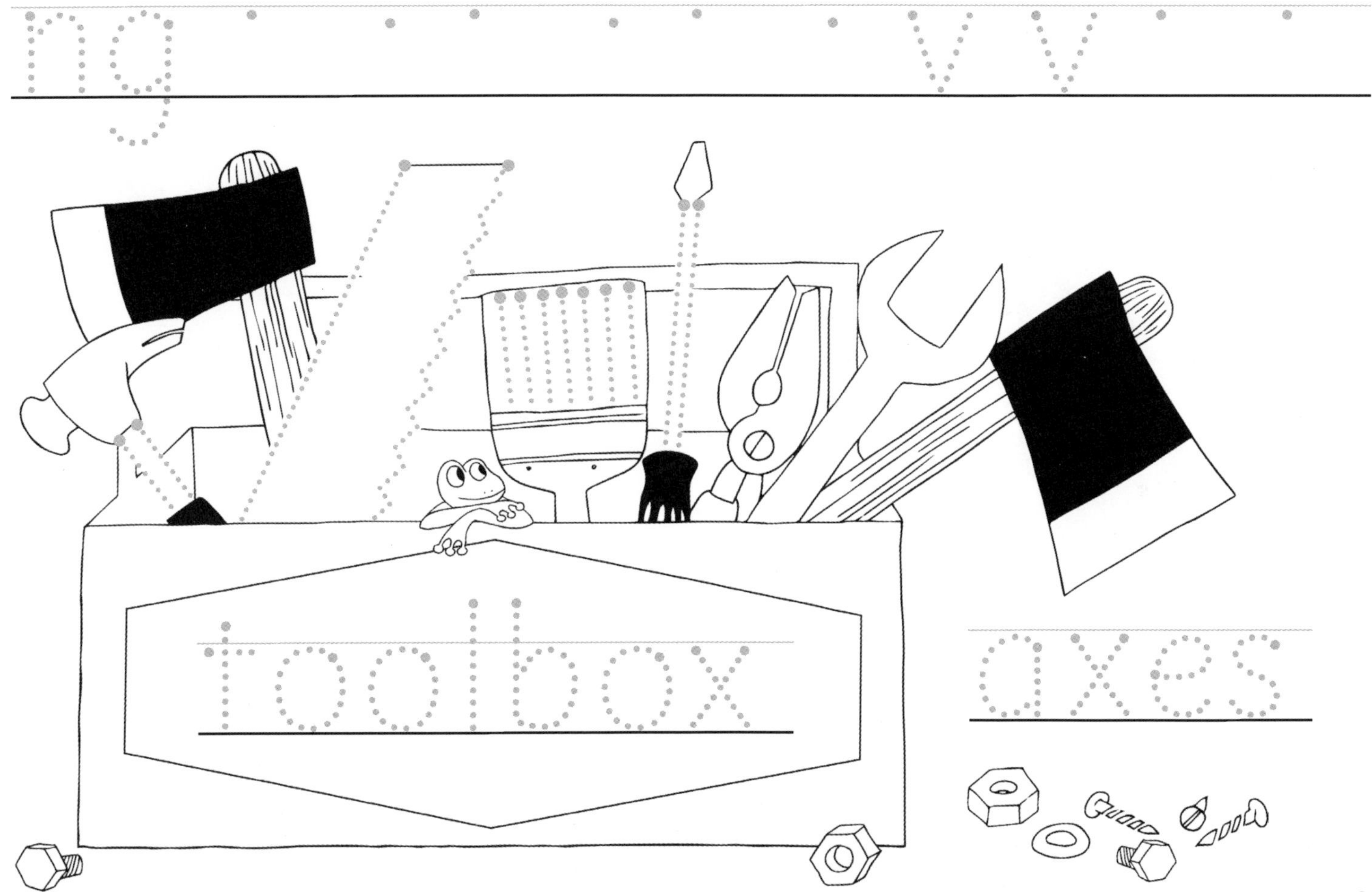
toolbox
axes

2
1
ch
These animals have a name that starts with /ch/. Can you think of any other /ch/ animals?
chimpanzees
ch ch ch

Help the chimp reach the big bunch of bananas.
Can you think of any fruits with the /ch/ sound in?

Help the worm reach the yam safely.

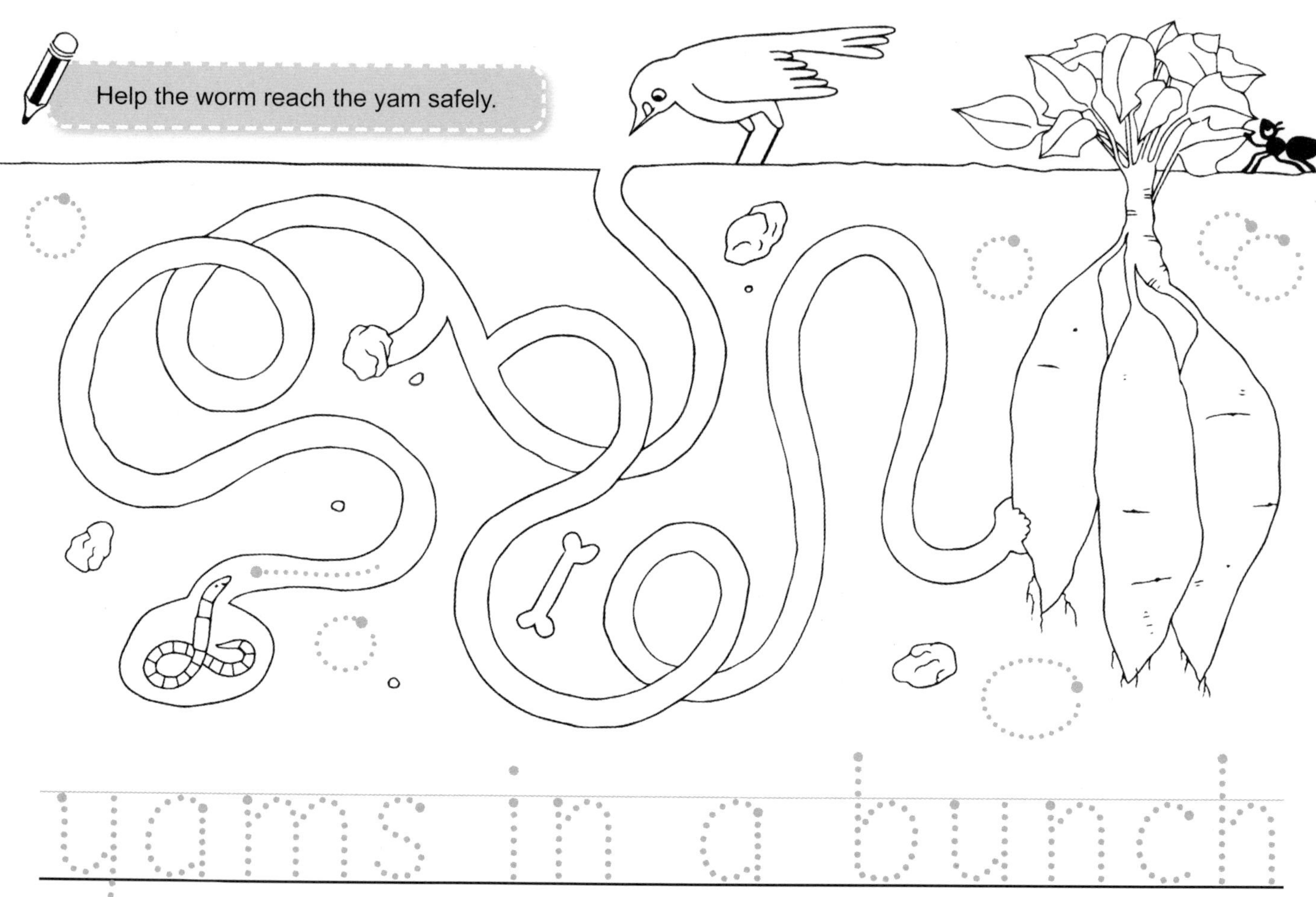

yams in a bunch

six big pumpkins

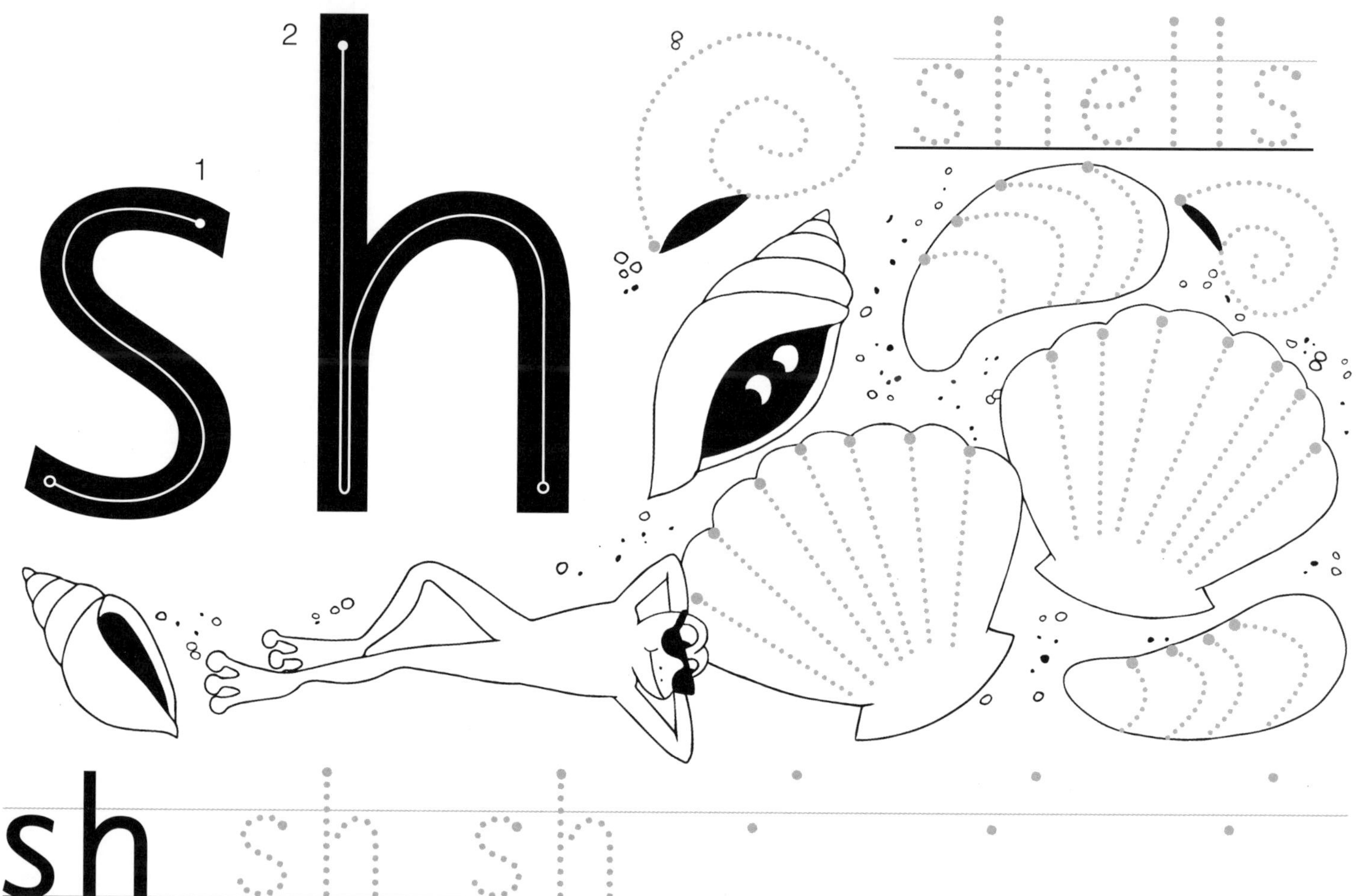
1
2
sh
shells
sh

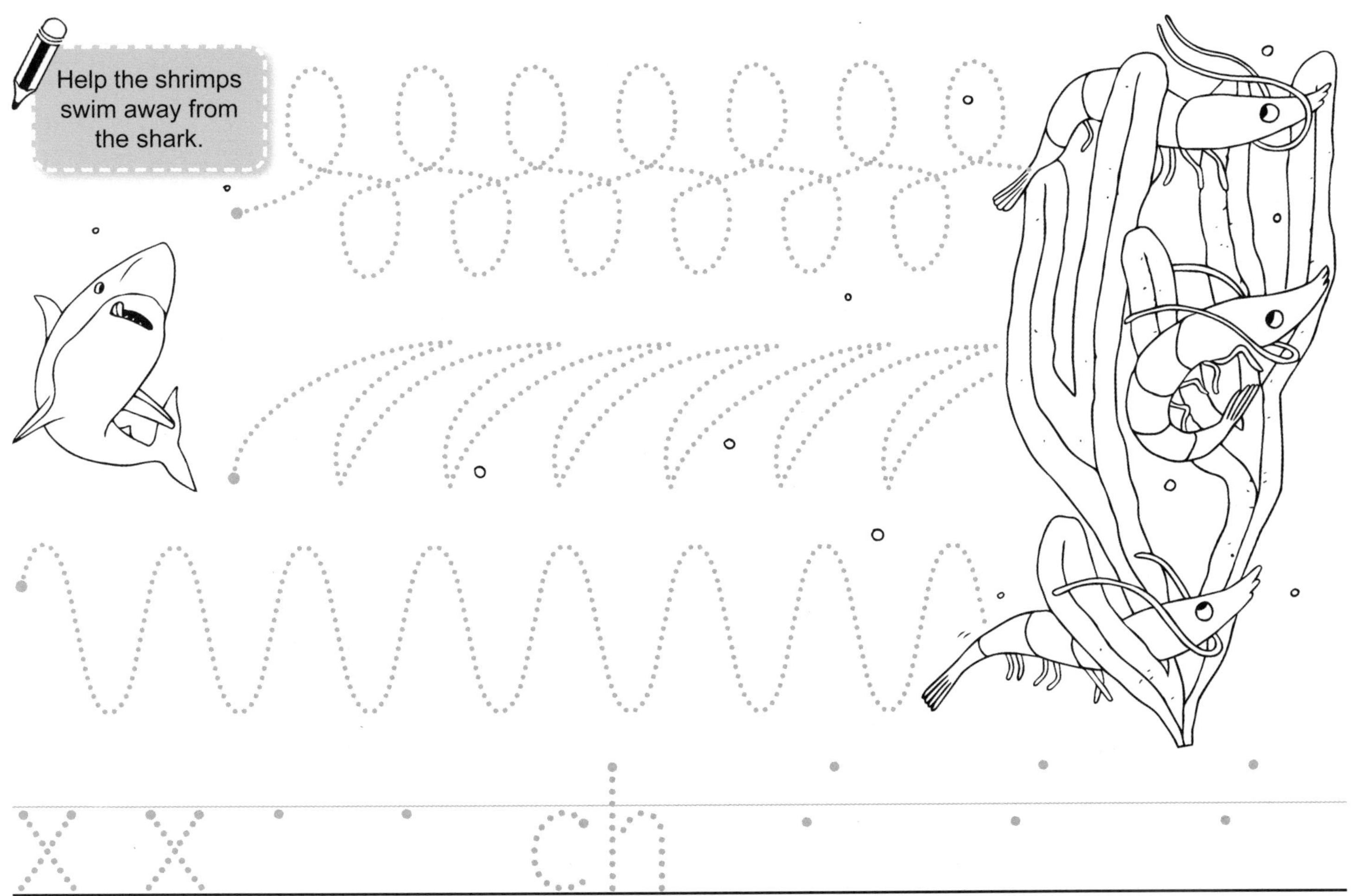
Help the shrimps swim away from the shark.

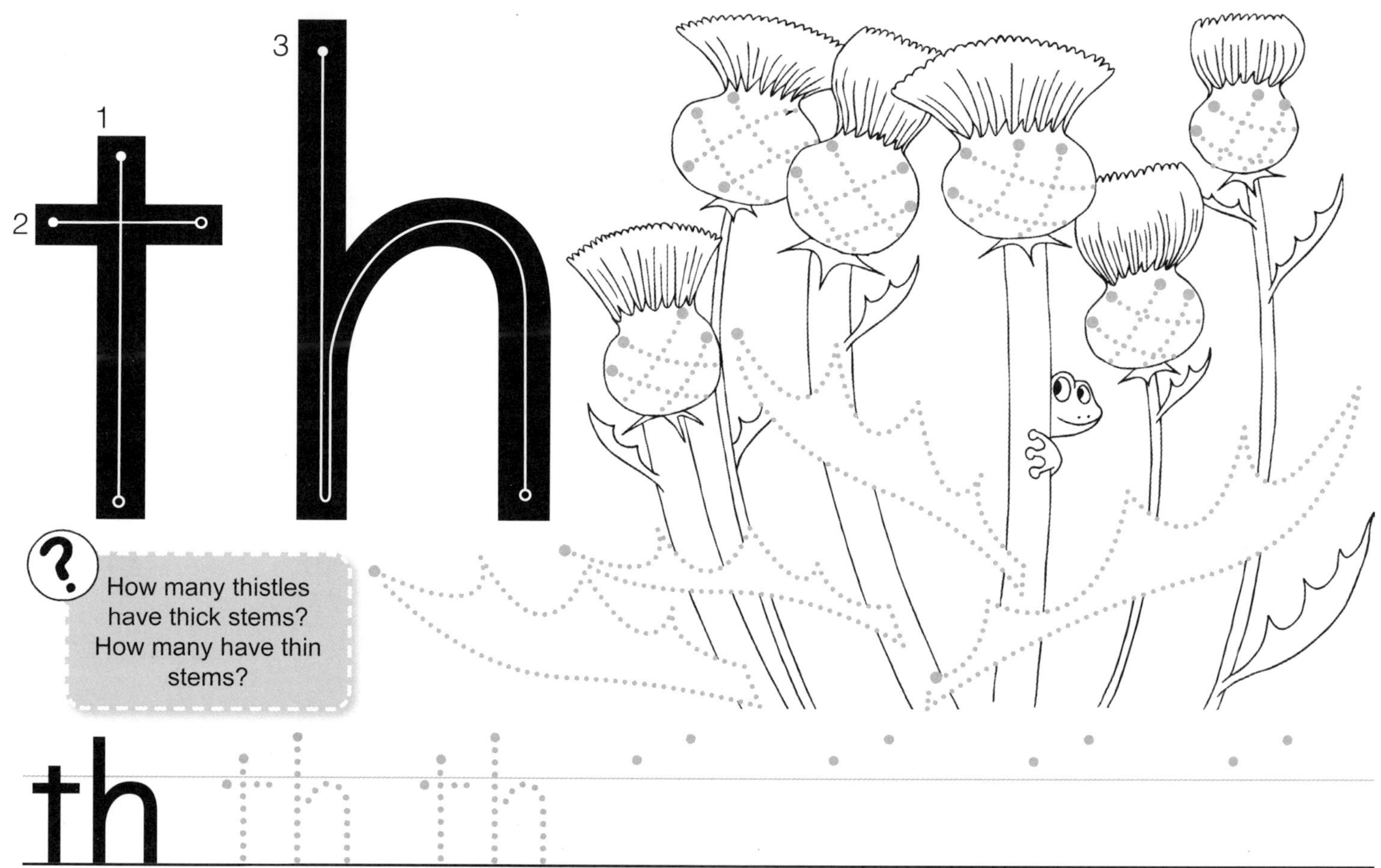
1
2
3
How many thistles have thick stems? How many have thin stems?

th

smooth

shopping list
mushrooms
chicken
toothbrush

Can you find everything written on the shopping list?

Practice writing your digraphs. Can you think of any other words with these sounds in them?

ch ch

chimp

sh sh

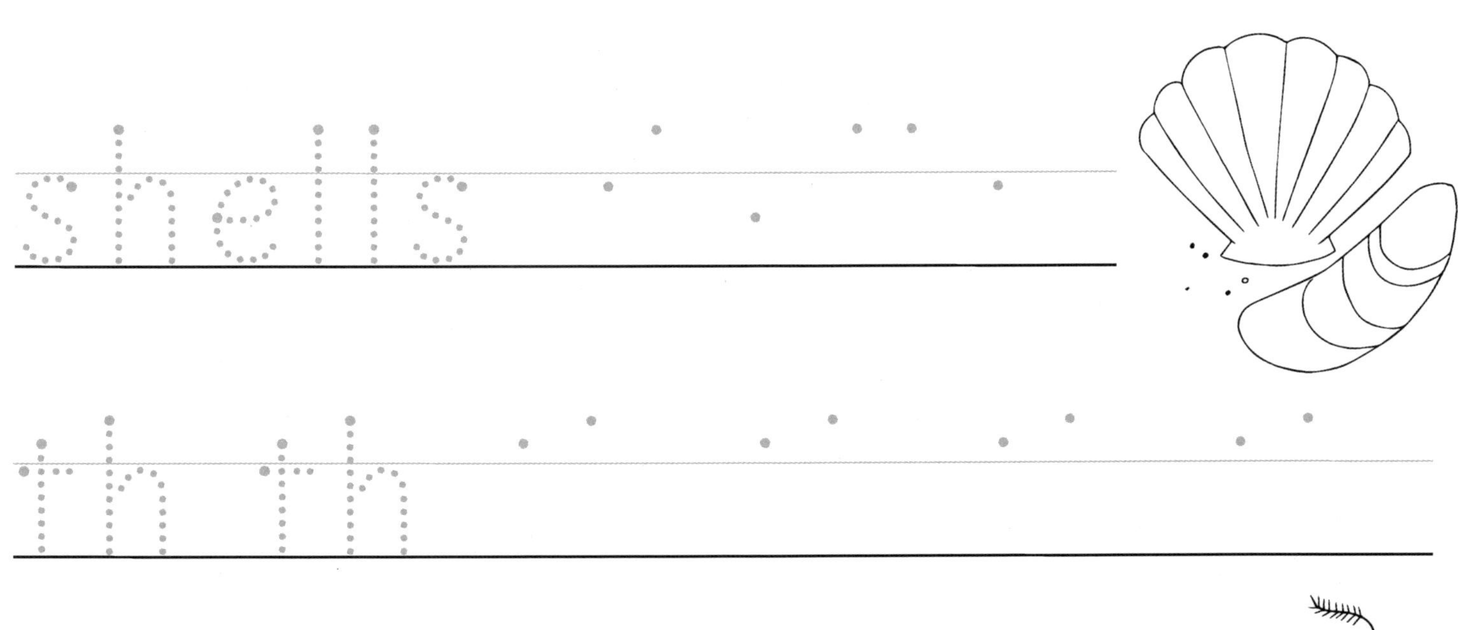
shells
th th
moth

Can you draw something that includes each sound?

y y y

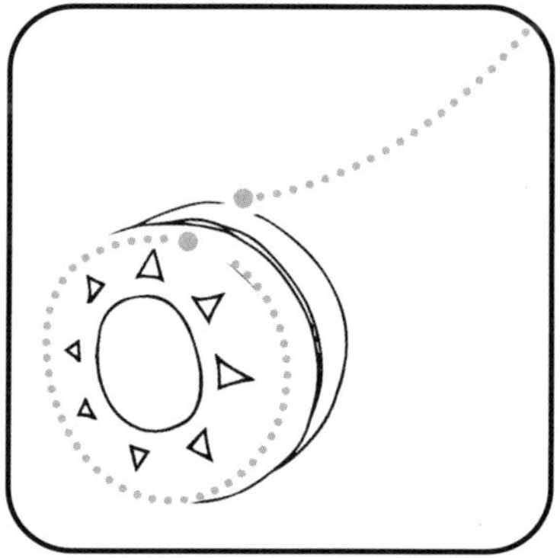

x x x

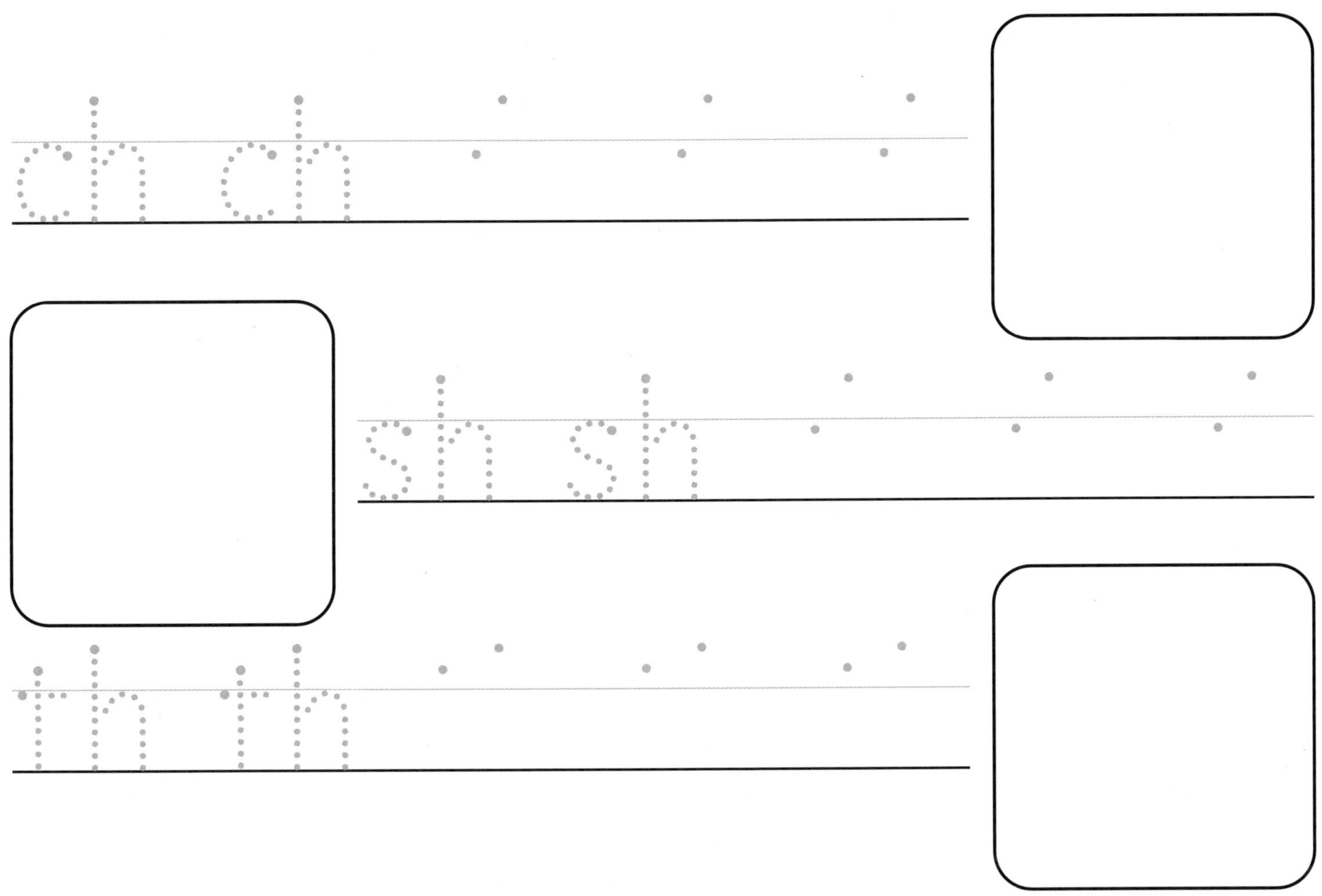

ch ch
sh sh
th th

Ages 4+

Jolly Phonics Handwriting Book

Perfect for practicing letter formation

These handwriting books provide letter formation practice for beginner writers. Dotted letters and words (with starting dots) remind students how the letters are formed, and encourage them to write words using the letter sounds they know. Each page features fun activities to complete and attractive pictures to color, which help the students to develop fine motor control.

This book contains the following letter sounds:

Group 1:	s a t i p n
Group 2:	c k e h r m d
Group 3:	g o u l f b
Group 4:	ai j oa ie ee or
Group 5:	z w ng v oo oo
Group 6:	y x ch sh th th
Group 7:	qu ou oi ue er ar

To see the full range of Jolly Phonics products, visit our website at www.jollylearning.com

MIX
Paper | Supporting responsible forestry
FSC® C016973

ISBN 978-1-83582-186-2

Reference: JL1862

82 Winter Sport Lane, Williston, VT 05495, USA. Tel: +1-800-488-2665
77 Hornbeam Road, Buckhurst Hill, Essex, IG9 6JX, UK. Tel: +44 20 8501 0405

www.jollylearning.com info@jollylearning.co.uk